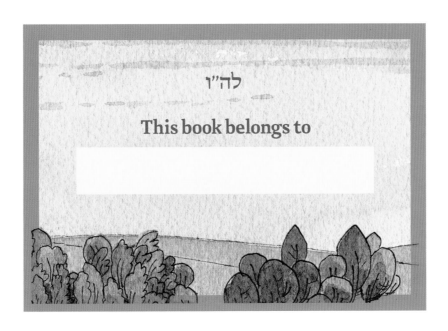

לה"ו

This book belongs to

BS"D

Sponsors
I would like to acknowledge the following people
who assisted me in the financing of the original artwork.

Marsha Alperin

Mark Donchin and Ruth Stone-Donchin

Moshe and Miriam Fishman
in memory of Basya Rochel bas Shmuel Hirsh ob"m

Joe and Marlyn Garfinkel
in memory of their parents: Chaim Yisroel and Celia Garfinkel;
Yosef Chaim and Chana Steinmetz

Ruth Gelman

Sandy Gilford

Lois Grayson

Mike and Alona Horowitz
in honor of their children

Jumpingballs.com (Daniel Najman)

Yrachmiel and Chana Kahn

Henrietta Klein

Bernice Lipsitz
in memory of her daughter Shaindel Faiga bas Nachman (Sharon Asher)

Aryeh and Yehudis Litvak

Basya Lokey
in memory of her mother Chava Tanya

Elazar and Shoshana Bracha Plotke

Alan and Marilyn Rich
Roth Plumbing 5747 Melrose Ave. L. A., CA 90038

Yossi and Yehudit Schneerson

The Chevra Kadisha of Los Angeles

Dedicated to my beloved friend

Rebbetzin Sarah Rochel Schochet a"h
who encouraged me to teach

and to

Bais Yaakov of Los Angeles
where I had the *z'chus* to impart the
uplifting lessons from the life of Elisha

Many people reviewed the manuscript and gave their recommendations:

In my family there are my husband Rabbi Chaim Zev Citron, my mother Hadassa Carlebach, my son Rabbi Aryeh Citron and his son Shragi, my son Rabbi Avraham and his wife Devora Leah Citron, and my daughter Nechama Dina Smith.

Among my friends Rachel Malkin, Sheindy Mordechai and her daughter Shoshi, and Rabbi Gershon Schusterman.

My sincerest gratitude to all!

Author's Note:
Source material for **The Miracles of Elisha**
The *Book of Kings I* and *II (Melachim I and II)* and its commentaries:
the *Midrash, Rashi, Metzudot, Radak, Malbim, Targum Yonatan, Ralbag,* and *Alshich Hakadosh.*

The Miracles of
ELISHA

by Sterna Citron

illustrated by Igor Eydel

1
Rich Farmer No More

In the Land of Israel, many years ago, there lived a prophet by the name of Eliyahu. With his long beard, flowing cape, and leather belt, he taught the Jewish people Torah, prayed for them, and made miracles for them.

One day G-d told Eliyahu to go to the village of Aveil Mechola. There he had to do something very important. He had to appoint the next prophet.

Eliyahu searched through the village. Finally, in the field of Shafat, he saw twelve men plowing, each with a pair of oxen. Behind the very last plow was his student Elisha, the son of Shafat.

Taking off his cape, Eliyahu walked to the back of the field and threw the cape over the young man's shoulders. Eliyahu kept walking as if he hadn't done anything.

Elisha understood. He dropped his plow and ran after Eliyahu.

"Let me kiss my father and mother good-bye," Elisha cried out excitedly. "Then I will follow you."

"Go back to your work!" Eliyahu said. "You don't have to come if you don't want to!" Eliyahu was testing him to see if he really wanted to come with him or not.

Of course, Elisha wanted to come! What could be better than to learn from Eliyahu how to be a prophet of the Jewish people?

He ran to his parents. "Eliyahu, the prophet, has come. He wants me to go with him," he said, kissing his mother and father good-bye. Being humble, he did not mention that he had been chosen to be the next prophet.

Shafat and his wife were so proud. Eliyahu himself had come for their son! Everyone knew about the holy man with his flowing cape. Everyone knew how he always prayed for the Jewish people and made miracles for them.

They said goodbye to their son, their eyes shining with tears of joy mixed with a bit of sadness. They were excited for him, but they would miss him, too. He was always so respectful. He was a good worker too. Now they would have to find someone else to plow the fields.

Happiest of all was Elisha. A couple of hours ago, he was the son of a farmer, plowing with his father's oxen, and now he was going to serve Eliyahu and learn from him. Eliyahu would show him how to truly love and fear G-d and would teach him how to take care of the Jewish people. How thankful Elisha was!

"Let me make a party for the people of the village before I go," he thought. He chopped up his plow for firewood, slaughtered the oxen, and cooked the meat over the fire.

"Everyone is invited to my party," the young man called out. "Please come, one and all!"

As he served his guests, Elisha's face beamed with joy. The guests said, "May you have success!" They were proud that someone from their village was going to be Eliyahu's special student.

With that, Elisha said goodbye to his village and to his old way of life. There would be no more rich home with many fields to plow. It was going to be a new kind of life. He was a little nervous. But Eliyahu would teach him what he had to know, and G-d would surely help.

2
Up, up in a Chariot of Fire

Eliyahu had been the prophet of the Jewish people for a long time. He had led them through good times and hard times.

Finally, the time came when he had to leave this world. But Eliyahu was not going to die like other people. G-d was going to take him up alive to heaven. Being humble, he did not tell that to anyone, not even to Elisha, his best student.

Before leaving this world, Eliyahu wanted to say good-bye to his students. There were 100 students, 50 in Beit El and 50 in Yericho.

"G-d has sent me to Beit El," Eliyahu said to Elisha, "but please stay here."

"As G-d lives and as your soul lives, I will not leave you," Elisha swore. Even though Eliyahu had not said anything, Elisha could sense with his holy spirit that his beloved teacher was going to leave the world that day. He wanted to be with him until the very last minute.

Since Elisha had sworn, Eliyahu had no choice but to take him along because, if not, Elisha would be breaking his vow. So Eliyahu and Elisha went together.

At Beit El, the students came out of the study hall. They, too, sensed that Eliyahu would be leaving the world that day. They asked him, "Did you know that today G-d is taking off the crown from your head?" They called Eliyahu the crown of Elisha's head because Elisha was so close to his master and respected him so much.

Elisha said, "Yes, I also know. Hush!"

Now it was time for Eliyahu to say good-bye to the students in Yericho.

"Please stay here because G-d has sent me to Yericho," Eliyahu said to Elisha.

Again Elisha swore that he would not leave him. Every moment with his master was precious! And so again Eliyahu had to take Elisha with him.

In Yericho, the other students came out. They, too, asked Elisha, "Did you know that today G-d is taking off the crown from your head?"

Again Elisha answered, "Yes, I also know. Hush!"

The hour had come for Eliyahu to go up to heaven. Eliyahu said to Elisha, "Please stay here, for G-d has sent me to the Jordan River." There, from the other side of the Jordan River, Eliyahu was going to be taken up alive to heaven.

Yet a third time that day, Elisha swore he was not going to leave Eliyahu. And so master and student went to the edge of the river.

They stopped at the water's edge while from afar the students of Yericho stood and watched. Taking his cape, Eliyahu folded it and struck the river. A miracle! The waters parted! Water was on the right and on the left, but in the middle it was dry.

Eliyahu and Elisha walked across the dry land to the other side of the river.

"Ask what I can do for you before I am taken from you," Eliyahu said to Elisha.

"I would like double your prophecy," Elisha answered.

"You asked for something difficult," said Eliyahu. "This is how you will know that you got your wish. If you see me going up, that is the sign you will get what you asked for. If you don't, you will not get it."

As the two holy men walked together, a chariot and horses of fire suddenly appeared. It came between them and carried Eliyahu up to the heavens.

And Elisha saw it happen! He watched Eliyahu go higher and higher, all the way up to the heavens!

"My master, my master," Elisha cried out, "you do more for Israel with your prayers than chariots and horsemen!"

He watched until he could not see his master anymore. Now Eliyahu was gone. His beloved teacher, the leader of the Jewish people, Eliyahu, the prophet, was gone. He tore his clothes as a sign of how sad he felt.

But then Elisha noticed something lying on the ground, right where the chariots and horses had been. Eliyahu's cape! Eliyahu had dropped it as he went up to Heaven. He had left it for him! Picking up the cape, Elisha walked back to the edge of the Jordan. He struck the river with the cape.

Nothing happened.

"Where is G-d, the G-d of Eliyahu?" he asked.

Just then the river split, exactly as it had split for Eliyahu. Elisha knew he had been given his wish to have double the power of his master. Before it had parted for two holy men, and now the river parted just for him.

Elisha walked across to the other side of the river.

The 50 students who had been watching came and bowed before the new prophet.

"The spirit of Eliyahu has rested on Elisha," they said.

3
The Search for Eliyahu

Elisha had seen Eliyahu go up to heaven, but the students had not. They had only seen the strong wind.

The students wondered what happened to Eliyahu. Perhaps he was still alive.

They said to Elisha, "Maybe the wind carried Eliyahu and set him down among the mountains or valleys. We are 50 strong men. Please let us go and look for Eliyahu."

Elisha knew it would be a waste of time for them to search for Eliyahu. After all, he had seen with his own eyes how Eliyahu went up in a chariot of fire. But if he told them that, it would be showing off because none of the other students had seen it.

He said, "Do not go."

The students begged and begged. Finally Elisha said, "Go."

They searched among the mountains and valleys. After three days, they gave up and came back to Elisha, all tired out.

"Didn't I tell you not to go?" Elisha asked.

Elisha never did tell the students his secret.

4
From Bitter to Sweet

The people of Yericho loved their city, but there was one problem. The water in their river was bitter, and anyone who drank from it would die. They did not know what to do.

The people of Yericho realized that right there in their city was Elisha, the new prophet. Here was their chance!

They came to Elisha and told him, "Our city is a nice place, as you can see, but the water is bad, and the people are dying."

"Bring me a new plate, and put salt in it," Elisha said.

A new plate and salt! They quickly ran and brought Elisha what he had asked for. They waited to see what he would do.

The prophet took the plate and salt to the spring where the river began. The people followed, eager to see what would happen. Before their curious eyes, the holy man threw the salt into the spring.

"So says G-d," he said as they all grew quiet. "I have cured these waters. From now on, there will be no more death and dying."

Immediately the water became sweet. Ahh, how good it tasted! Now the thirsty people of Yericho could drink without fear.

But the people of Yericho did not understand. How did throwing salt into the spring make the river sweet? But some people understood. Salt is like the bad within a person, and the spring is like the Torah. Elisha was teaching them to throw their bad ways into the sweet spring of Torah.

And so the people of Yericho returned to studying the Torah. And from that day on, nobody died from drinking the water. Just as Elisha had promised, the water of the Yericho River stayed sweet until today.

This was Elisha's second miracle. Eliyahu's promise was coming true.

5
The Bears and the Forest

Elisha was walking along the road from Yericho to Beit El when he met a group of 42 men, all water carriers. Upon seeing Elisha, they made fun of him. They were angry because he had made the waters of Yericho sweet. Before, when the water was bitter, they sold water to the people of Yericho. Now that the river water was sweet, no one needed to buy their water anymore.

Oh, how they hated Elisha! They did not care that people had been dying from the bitter water and now they would not die anymore. They only cared that they could not sell their water.

"Get away from here, baldy!" they yelled at Elisha.

They called him "baldy" because he did not have long hair like Eliyahu. They wanted him to feel he wasn't as good a prophet as Eliyahu.

Elisha turned around to look at the people making fun of him. He wanted to punish them, but he had to check first if they had done any *mitzvot*. If so, he wouldn't punish them. Seeing with his holy spirit that they had never done any *mitzvot*, Elisha cursed them with G-d's name.

Suddenly, two wild bears rushed out of the forest and killed the men who had mocked the prophet.

This was a miracle because never before had there been bears in that forest. In fact, never before had there been a forest there! It was a double miracle which G-d made so that the prophet's decree would come true.

But Elisha should not have cursed them even though they were bad people. He was punished for that, and for the first time in his life he got sick.

When he became well, Elisha went to the mountain of Carmel and from there to Shomron, the capital of the kingdom of Israel.

6

Elisha Goes to War

In the Land of Israel in those days, there were two kingdoms, each with its own king. Yehoshafat, the king over Judah and Benjamin, was a good king who believed in G-d. He never bowed down to idols like so many other people did in those times. He was called the king of Judah.

The king over the other ten tribes was Yehoram, the king of Israel. Yehoram was a wicked king who worshipped idols as his parents, King Achav and Queen Izevel, had done.

One day Yehoram received frightening news. Meisha, king of Moav, refused to pay Israel taxes. He was rebelling!

G-d made Moav rebel so that Yehoram would return to G-d and stop worshipping idols. If Yehoram returned to G-d, all the ten tribes would return to G-d too.

But Yehoram did not stop worshipping idols. Instead, he got ready to go to war against Moav. He counted the soldiers in his army to see how many there were even though counting people is forbidden by the Torah.

Yehoram thought he did not have enough soldiers to fight against Moav. He sent a message to Yehoshafat, the king of Judah, saying, "Moav rebelled against me. Will you come with me to fight against them?"

The good king of Yehudah wanted to help. He sent back a message saying, "Whatever you do, I will do. My soldiers are your soldiers. My horses are your horses. Which way will we go?"

"We will go through the desert of Edom," Yehoram answered. He planned to ask the army of Edom to join, too. Then he would surely win the war against the nation of Moav.

Edom was not a friend of Israel, but Edom hated Moav. So Edom joined the soldiers of Israel and Judah.

For seven days the three armies marched through the dry, hot desert on their way to Moav.

The sun beat down on their heads. There was no water to drink for the soldiers and their animals. Yehoram saw how weak and thirsty the soldiers were. If the soldiers were so weak, how would they be able to fight?

"Woe to us!" cried the king of Israel. "G-d wants us to fall into Moav's hands!"

But the king of Yehudah did not lose his faith in G-d. "Is there a prophet here?" he asked. "Let us ask the prophet to tell us what G-d says!"

"There is a prophet here!" said one of Yehoram's servants. "Elisha, son of Shafat, who served Eliyahu, is here with us!"

Yehoshafat called out happily, "Elisha will tell us G-d's word, of course!"

Sure enough, Elisha was there. He had quietly joined the army. War was dangerous, and perhaps he could be of help. And maybe, just maybe, he could get Yehoram to do *teshuvah*.

The three kings went to the prophet to hear the word of G-d. Yehoshafat came humbly in regular clothes, but the proud Yehoram came dressed in his royal garments.

When Elisha saw Yehoram, he got upset. Only Yehoshafat had asked for a prophet. Yehoram hadn't even thought of it!

"Why are you coming to me? Go to the false prophets of your father and mother!" Elisha said angrily to Yehoram.

"Don't say that! And don't mention my sins," Yehoram begged. "Pray that G-d have pity on us, for G-d has surely given us into the hands of Moav!"

Yehoram's words made Elisha even more angrier. Where was Yehoram's faith?

"By the life of G-d, the Master of all armies, before whom I stand in prayer," the prophet said, "I wouldn't even look at you if it were not for Yehoshafat, the king of Yehudah!"

Elisha waited to hear the word of G-d. The three kings waited too. But the word of G-d did not come to Elisha because G-d doesn't speak to someone when he is angry.

Minutes went by, and still nothing.

"Bring me a musician," the prophet said.

A musician was brought, When he began playing, Elisha finally became calm. The word of G-d came to him.

"So says G-d," Elisha told the three kings, "'the valley will be filled with pools of water. You won't see any wind, you won't see any rain, but the valley will be filled with water. And you will drink, and your cattle and animals will drink. But all that will be a small miracle for G-d. The big miracle will be that G-d will give Moav into your hands.'"

The kings were overjoyed.

Then Elisha told them what G-d said they must do. They must destroy the cities of Moav, stop up their springs, fill up their plowed fields with rocks, and chop down their fruit trees. Chopping down fruit trees is usually forbidden, but in this case G-d commanded them to do so to punish Moav for rebelling.

The next day, just at the time when the morning sacrifice was being brought in the *Beit Hamikdash*, the first miracle happened. There was no wind, there was no rain, but suddenly from the country of Edom, water flowed into the valley like a river. All around were pools filled with water, just as the prophet had said there would be.

The thirsty people and animals had plenty to drink. The soldiers felt strong again.

Meanwhile, the Moavites heard that the armies were coming. Every Moavite man and boy old enough to fight gathered at the border of their land. They waited impatiently for the armies to come.

But a strange thing happened. When the sun rose and lit up the valley, the pools of water in the desert looked red. The Moavites standing at the border saw the pools and yelled, "It's blood! The three kings and their armies must have gotten into a fight and killed each other. Let's go get their spoils!" All those horses, all that gold, all that silver — it would all be theirs!

They dropped their swords and raced to the other side of the border. Each Moavite wanted to be there first to get as much silver, gold, and horses as he could.

But what a surprise the Moavites had! The pools of blood turned out to be water, and the Jewish soldiers were not dead but alive. In fact, they stood, swords in hand, ready to fight. The Jews were able to win easily because the Moavite soldiers had left their swords behind in their rush.

The Jewish soldiers did what Elisha had told them to do. They destroyed the cities of Moav, chopped down the trees, stopped up the springs, and filled up the plowed fields with rocks. The only thing left were the stones of the walls of the biggest city, Charoshes, and they destroyed those too.

Meisha, the king, was very angry. His army was losing! He was especially angry at Edom. Why had they come to fight against Moav? This war had nothing to do with them, only with the Jews!

Wanting to kill the king of Edom, Meisha took 700 of his strongest soldiers and tried to get to the king of Edom, but the Jews and Edomites fought strongly, and he could not reach the Edomite king.

Meisha, however, succeeded in capturing the son of the king of Edom. He took the young man to the top of the wall of the city. There he killed him for all to see.

The king of Edom became angry at the Jews. "Why didn't you do something to save my son?" he yelled. He decided to take his army and leave the war.

Having lost the help of Edom, the kings of Israel and Yehudah felt they had to give up the war, and so they went back to the Land of Israel. Moab had not been recaptured.

7
Lots of Pots

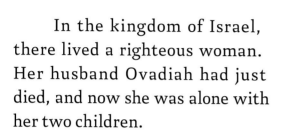

In the kingdom of Israel, there lived a righteous woman. Her husband Ovadiah had just died, and now she was alone with her two children.

Ovadiah had been one of the student-prophets of Eliyahu. He had brought food and drink to the other students in the caves of Beis El and Yericho, where they were hiding from the wicked Queen Izevel who was trying to kill them. Ovadiah also brought the students olive oil so they could study Torah by its light.

To pay for all the food, Ovadiah had to borrow money from Yehoram, who was then the prince. Yehoram made Ovadiah pay interest, which is forbidden by the Torah.

When Ovadiah died, Yehoram, who was now the king, wanted his money back. He sent a message to Ovadiah's widow saying, "If you don't pay me back the money and interest your husband owed me, I will take your two children as slaves!"

The woman did not know what to do. She didn't have the money with which to repay him. All she had in the house was a little bit of olive oil. But she was sure of one thing. "No matter what," she said to herself, "I will never, ever let my children be slaves to that idol-worshipping king!"

Every day the hard-hearted king sent her the same message. "Give me the money, or your children are mine!"

She needed help, and fast. But who could help?

"I will go to my husband's grave and pour out my troubles," she said to herself. She knew that her husband had been a holy man and that he had truly feared G-d. Surely, Ovadiah would help her!

She went with her children to the grave of her husband. She lay down on his grave and cried bitterly.

"Master, master," she called out to the soul of her husband, "where is your promise to me? Before you died, I asked you, 'Who will take care of me and the two children?' You told me that the Master of the Universe who takes care of all widows and orphans will also take care of us. But no one is taking care of us!"

Her children cried too. "Listen to us, father!" they said. "Listen to us!"

Suddenly, the voice of Ovadiah came from the grave.

"Go to Elisha," the voice said, "and ask him to bless you. Bring him the little bit of olive oil that you have in the house. When I hid the 100 students in the two caves and gave them food and water, I also brought them oil so they could learn Torah by its light. Let the prophet tell G-d about that, and G-d will repay you what I lent Him."

The widow did what her husband said. She went to Elisha with the jug of oil. "You knew my husband feared G-d," she said. "He not only fed the 100 students who were hiding, but he gave them oil so they could learn Torah by its light. Now Yehoram wants his money back, and, if not, he will take my children as slaves. I cannot bear the thought of my children growing up in the house of that idol worshipper!"

"What do you have in your house?" asked Elisha.

"I have nothing — just this small jug with only enough olive oil to smear on my little finger," she answered.

"Go to all your neighbors," Elisha said, "and borrow lots of empty pots. Don't borrow just a few. Borrow many! When you and your children get home, close the door behind you and the children. Then pour the oil from your jug into the pots. As soon as one pot gets filled, move it over, and put another one in its place."

Ovadiah's widow did as Elisha said. She went to her neighbors and borrowed pots. Lots of them. Big ones, little ones, tall ones, short ones.

She brought the pots home and carefully closed the door behind her and the children, just as the prophet had told her. She held the small jug with the olive oil in her hand while her children brought her the first pot. As she began pouring, a miracle happened. The empty pot quickly filled up to the top with bright, shiny olive oil!

The children ran and put a second pot in its place, then a third, and then a fourth. Like a fountain that never stops, the little jug just kept giving more oil!

Back and forth the children ran, carrying one empty pot after another.

When one pot filled up, the children moved it aside to make room for the next. Five, six, seven, eight. Soon they stopped counting, there were so many pots filled with olive oil.

"Bring me another pot," their mother said.

"There are no more," answered her son. The moment he said that, the jug stopped giving forth oil.

Ovadiah's wife went to Elisha and told him how all the pots miraculously filled up with oil.

"What should I do now?" she asked.

"Go and sell the oil in the market," said Elisha. "Then pay back Yehoram all the money you owe him. There will be enough money left for you and your children to live on for the rest of your lives."

Ovadiah's wife did as Elisha told her. She took her oil to the marketplace and sold it. Because olive oil was selling for a very high price that day, she made a lot of money.

The widow went to King Yehoram and paid him back the money. No more would she have to be afraid of his taking her children away!

Just as Elisha had promised, she had plenty of money left for her and her family to live on for the rest of their lives.

Elisha had performed another miracle, saving a Jewish woman and her children.

8
Elisha and the Woman from Shunam

Elisha often traveled to different towns and villages to see where he could help people. One of the towns he visited was Shunam. In Shunam, there lived a kind and rich woman. Whenever Elisha came to town, she and her husband always invited him to stay with them.

One day the woman said to her husband, "Elisha is a holy man. We should make him a room of his own. Let's build a little room in the attic for him with a bed, table, chair, and lamp."

Her husband thought it was a good idea, and so the Shunamis woman had a small room built in the attic. In it she put a bed, a table, a chair, and a lamp. And whenever the prophet came to town, he stayed in that room.

Elisha was very grateful. He wanted to do something for the woman who was so kind. "Call the Shunamis woman," Elisha said to Geichazi, his servant.

Geichazi called the woman, and she came to Elisha.

"You were so kind to me," Elisha said. "What can I do for you? Shall I speak to the king or the general for you? Do you need anything from them?"

"I don't need anyone to speak to the king or general for me," the woman answered. "I live in peace among my friends and relatives."

When the woman left, the prophet asked his servant, "So what can we do to repay her?"

"She has no children," Geichazi answered, "and her husband is getting old."

Elisha told Geichazi to call the Shunamis woman again. She came and stood at the door to Elisha's room.

"Just as you are alive now, so will you be alive this time next year, hugging a little boy," the prophet blessed her.

The Shunamis woman cried out, "Man of G-d, please don't promise me something that won't happen!"

A year later, Elisha's blessing came true. The woman gave birth to a baby boy. She and her husband were overjoyed.

The little boy grew. One day he went out with his father to the field where the reapers were working.

Suddenly the boy felt sick. "My head, my head!" he moaned.

"Carry him home to his mother," his father said to one of the workers.

All morning, the Shunamis woman held her son in her lap and prayed. But the child got sicker and sicker. At noon, he died.

Without saying a word to anyone, she carried the boy upstairs to Elisha's room, laid him down on Elisha's bed, and closed the door.

"Please get me one of the servant boys and a donkey," she said to her husband. I will hurry to the man of G-d and come back."

"Why are you going today?" her husband asked. "It isn't Rosh Chodesh or Shabbos." That was when his wife usually went to hear words of Torah from the prophet.

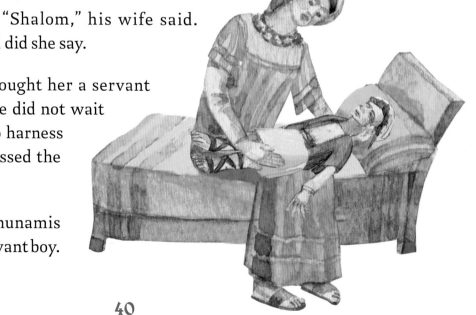

"Shalom," his wife said. And not another word did she say.

Her husband brought her a servant boy and a donkey. She did not wait for the servant boy to harness the donkey but harnessed the donkey herself.

"Go fast," the Shunamis woman said to the servant boy.

"Don't stop or slow down unless I tell you to."

They hurried to the Carmel mountain where Elisha would pray and study the holy Torah.

From afar, Elisha saw the Shunamis woman coming up the mountain. Something terrible must have happened! He said to his servant Geichazi, "There is the Shunamis woman. Run and ask her, 'Are you well? Is your husband well? Is your son well?'"

Geichazi ran and asked her, but all the Shunamis woman would answer was "Shalom." When she reached the prophet, she fell to the ground and held on to Elisha's feet. Geichazi tried to push her away, but the Shunamis woman would not let go.

Elisha said to his servant, "Leave her alone because her soul is bitter. And I do not know why, for G-d has hidden it from me."

Finally the woman spoke. "Did I ask my master for a child?" she cried. "Didn't I say not to disappoint me?"

Suddenly Elisha understood.

"Be quick," Elisha said to Geichazi. "Take my staff in your hand, and go. If anyone says hello to you, don't answer. Put my staff on the boy's face."

Geichazi left immediately, but the Shunamis woman stayed. "As G-d lives and as your soul lives, I am not leaving you," she said to Elisha.

Geichazi rushed down the mountain, Elisha's staff in his hand. On the way, he met some people. "Hello," they said. "Where are you going in such a hurry?"

"Hello," he said, "Would you believe my master sent me to bring the dead back to life?"

"Really?" they asked, their eyes wide.

"Really!" he said.

When Geichazi reached the house of the Shunamis woman, he went upstairs to Elisha's room. Geichazi put the staff on the boy's face, but nothing happened. The boy did not come back to life.

Geichazi went back up the mountain to Elisha. "The boy did not wake up," he said.

Elisha did not wait a second. Down the mountain they went, he and the woman from Shunam. When he came to the house, he went up to his room in the attic where the child lay and closed the door.

Elisha prayed. "Master of the Universe," he said, "just as You made miracles through my master Eliyahu and just as Eliyahu brought the dead back to life, so may this boy come back to life."

Elisha stretched himself over the child. He put his mouth on the boy's mouth, his eyes on the boy's eyes, and his hands on the boy's hands.

The child's body began to get warm.

The prophet stood up. He walked back and forth across the room. Once more he prayed. Once more he stretched himself out on the child.

All of a sudden, the child sneezed—not once, not twice, but seven times. He opened up his eyes.

"Call the Shunamis woman," Elisha said to Geichazi.

The Shunamis woman came.

"Take your son," said Elisha.

The mother fell down before Elisha's feet. She could not say a word. She bowed down to show thanks to G-d, lifted her son, and carried him out.

When the child grew up, he was known as the prophet Habakkuk.

9
Poison in the Stew

Elisha was in Gilgal teaching his students. There was a famine in the land and not a lot of food to eat. G-d had caused the famine to happen because He wanted the king and the people of Israel to stop worshipping idols and return to Him.

Elisha was worried about the Shunamis woman who had been so kind to him. Elisha wanted to make sure she and her family would be all right during the long famine.

He sent her a message. "There will be a famine in the land for seven years. You must leave the Land of Israel. Go to another country, and stay there until the famine is over."

The Shunamis woman did as Elisha said. She and her family moved to the land of the Plishtim until the famine would be over.

Meanwhile, Elisha's students were hungry. Elisha said to a servant, "Set the big pot over the fire, and cook up a stew for the students."

The servant wondered what would go into the pot. There was hardly any food. But he listened to Elisha and set up a large pot, filled it with water, and put it on the fire.

Another student went out to the field to gather greens. He saw mushrooms growing near a wild grapevine. "How nice it would be to have them in the stew!" he thought.

Spreading out his coat, the student filled it with mushrooms and went back to the Yeshiva. He tore the mushrooms into small pieces and dropped them into the pot with the greens.

When it was done cooking, the hungry students began eating. Ugh! It was so bitter!

"Man of G-d," the students cried out to Elisha, "there's death in the pot! It's poisonous!"

"Pour the stew back into the pot," said the prophet, "and bring me flour."

The students poured their stew back into the pot and quickly brought Elisha flour. He threw it into the pot. "Pour stew for everyone, and let them eat it!" he said.

The servant poured out the stew again and the students tasted it. Sure enough, it wasn't bitter anymore. They ate the stew and were satisfied.

Their beloved master had performed another miracle.

10
Enough and More

The hunger in the land was growing worse. Food was getting harder to find.

One day a man from Baal Shalisha came with a gift for Elisha. He brought 20 rolls of barley bread and some roasted barley kernels.

Elisha was happy. "Give it to the students, and let them eat," he said to the servant.

"How can 20 rolls feed 100 people?" asked the servant.

The prophet answered, "Give it to them, for G-d said, 'There will be enough, and there will even be leftovers.'"

What could the servant do? He had to obey even though he could not see how a few rolls and some roasted barley could satisfy 100 hungry young men.

The servant gave out the rolls and roasted barley to the students. A miracle happened, and there was enough food for everyone! There was even food left over, just as the prophet had promised.

Yet another miracle of Elisha's had just taken place.

11
The General of Aram Pays a Visit

To the north of the Land of Israel was the country of Aram. At night, soldiers from Aram would sneak into Israel and rob Jewish homes.

One time, Naaman, the general of Aram, and his soldiers crossed the border into Israel and kidnapped a Jewish girl. Naaman took her to be a servant for his wife. For kidnapping the girl, G-d punished the general. Naaman became sick with *tzaraat*, a disease of the skin.

Naaman visited many doctors. None of them could help.

Feeling sorry for him, the Jewish girl said to Naaman's wife, "Why doesn't your husband go to the prophet in Shomron? He will surely cure him from his *tzaraat!*"

Naaman liked the idea. Maybe he would be healed! He went to the king of Aram and told him what the Jewish girl had said.

"Go," said the king. "I will write a letter for you to bring to the king of Israel." The king of Israel would be able to arrange for Naaman to see Elisha.

The king of Aram wrote a letter to Yehoram, and sent it with the general.

Naaman also took ten talents of silver, six thousand pieces of gold, and ten sets of clothing as a gift for

Elisha. He set out together with servants, chariots, and horses to the capital city of Shomron. There Naaman gave the king of Israel the letter.

Yehoram read the letter. It said, "I have sent you my general Naaman. Please cure him from his *tzaraat*."

The king of Israel turned pale. "Does the king of Aram think I am G-d that I can make someone live or die?" he asked. "How can I cure him from *tzaraat*? The king of Aram must be looking for an excuse to start a war!"

He was so upset he tore his clothes in mourning. He had just finished a war with Moav. He did not want a new war with Aram!

And because the king did not believe in the prophet, he did not think of sending Naaman to him.

Miles away, Elisha knew with his holy spirit what happened. He sent Yehoram a message: "Why did you tear your clothes? Let Naaman come to me so he should know there is a prophet in Israel!"

The king was not sure about the miraculous powers of the prophet, but he was happy that he wasn't expected to cure the general. So he sent Naaman to Elisha.

When the general came to Elisha's home, he knocked at the door. He and his servants waited for Elisha.

A messenger appeared. He said, "Go and wash in the Yarden River seven times. Then your skin will be like it used to be, and you will be cured."

49

Naaman's face became red with anger. He had expected the prophet to come out, not a messenger. After all, Naaman was a general, and not just any general, but the favorite general of the king of Aram!

Anyway, what was special about the Yarden? "The rivers of Aram are a lot better than the rivers of Israel!" shouted Naaman. "I'll wash in those rivers and get pure!" He was so angry, he was ready to turn back and go home.

Naaman's servants tried to calm him down. "My master," said one of his servants, "if the prophet had asked you to do a very hard thing, wouldn't you do it? All he's asking is for you to wash in the river. Why not try it?"

"Fine," said Naaman. "I'll do it."

He went down to the river and dipped in seven times. Lo and behold, his skin became clear like the skin of a baby. His *tzaraat* was gone!

Now Naaman understood that Elisha was a true prophet and that the Land of Israel and its rivers were special and holy.

Standing before the prophet, the general humbly said, "Now I know that the only true G-d is the G-d of Israel."

Elisha was happy to hear these words from the general.

Naaman brought out the gold, silver, and clothing. "Here is a present from your servant," he said.

The prophet did not want the general to think he cured him to get presents from him. "I swear by G-d that I will not take it," he said.

Naaman begged him to take the gifts, but the prophet refused. Finally Naaman gave up and prepared to return home.

"I want to build an altar out of earth from *the Land of Israel,*" Naaman said to Elisha. "May I have some earth from this holy land? From now on, I'm only going to serve G-d, and no other gods."

"Yes, you may," Elisha said with a smile. He hoped that Naaman would go back to his country and teach the king of Aram about the one true G-d.

The general had one more request from Elisha. "When the king of Aram bows down at the temple of Rimon, he leans on me, and that makes me bow down too," he said. "Please ask G-d to forgive me for that." Naaman wanted to do everything right now.

"Go in peace," Elisha said.

After Naaman and his servants gathered some earth, they climbed into their chariots and got ready to leave.

Watching all this was Geichazi, Elisha's servant. He saw Naaman leave, taking his gifts back with him. What a shame, Geichazi thought. All that gold! All that silver! Just one silver talent was worth 1,500 silver coins. He could buy so many things with just one talent!

"Since my master would not take any of the presents, I swear I will run after Naaman and take some of them," Geichazi said to himself.

He snuck out quietly so Elisha would not know. Only Geichazi's sons knew, and they did not try to stop him.

By now Naaman was about a mile away. Geichazi ran after him as fast as he could.

Noticing someone running after him, the general leaned out of his chariot and called out, "Is everything okay?"

"Everything is okay," Geichazi answered. "My master sent me to tell you that two new students arrived from Mount Ephraim. We need a talent of silver and two new sets of clothing."

Naaman did not know if Geichazi was telling the truth or not. Hadn't Elisha sworn he would not take any gifts? "Swear to me that your master sent you!" said the general.

"I swear," said Geichazi.

Well, then, he must be telling the truth, Naaman thought. "Take two talents of silver," he said.

"No, no," answered Geichazi, "one talent is enough." But secretly he hoped Naaman would give him two.

Naaman poured the silver coins into two pouches—two whole talents' worth! He tied the coins up in a cloth and gave it to a couple of servants to carry together with the clothing.

Geichazi led the servants to a dark hiding-place where he hid the gifts. Then Geichazi went back and stood before Elisha as if nothing had happened.

"Where are you coming from, Geichazi?" asked the prophet. "Don't you realize that my heart knew when Naaman leaned out of his chariot to talk to you?" Elisha asked. "Is now the right time—after such a miracle—to take silver and clothing to buy yourself olive orchards and vineyards, sheep and cattle, servants and handmaidens?"

How upset Elisha was! He had hoped the king of Aram would make peace with Israel after seeing how he had cured his general for free. Now there would be no peace.

Elisha cursed Geichazi with a terrible curse. "May the *tzaraat* of Naaman go on to you and your sons forever," he said.

Suddenly, *tzaraat* covered Geichazi. His skin became a horrible white, exactly how Naaman's skin had been. Geichazi turned around and left, never to come back.

Did Elisha do the right thing to curse his servant with tzaraat? Yes, Geichazi had taken money that was not his. He had lied to Naaman and to Elisha. He had sworn falsely. Yes, he needed to be punished, but the punishment the prophet gave him was too severe, and because of that Elisha became sick for the second time in his life.

12
The Axe that Floated

When Geichazi was in charge of Elisha's Yeshiva, there were only a few students. Now that he was gone, many new students came. In a short time, the Yeshiva grew from 100 students to 2,000!

Soon there was not enough room for everyone.

"The school is too small for us," the students said. "Let's go to the Jordan River, get logs, and build ourselves a new building for the Yeshiva."

They asked Elisha for permission, and he agreed. They wanted him to come with them, and he agreed to that too.

And so teacher and students went down to the edge of the river. Everyone was excited to be building a new and bigger building for the Yeshiva.

The students took their axes and swung away at the trees. The forest was filled with the sound of chopping and sawing. As the young men worked, they sang, laughed, and joked. It was a joyful time.

All of a sudden, an axe slipped out of the hand of one of the students and fell into the water. The student watched, his mouth open in shock, as the axe sank down to the bottom of the river.

"Oh, no, my master!" he cried out to Elisha. "That axe was borrowed!"

The student felt very bad. He did not have money to buy a new axe to give back to his friend.

Elisha came immediately to the student, the rest of the students following.

"Where did it fall?" the prophet asked.

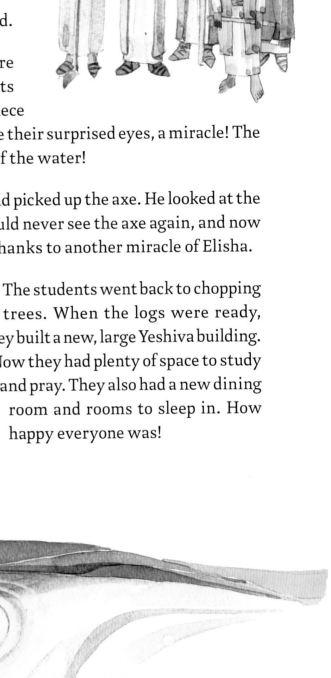

The young man showed Elisha where the axe had slipped and fallen. The students watched eagerly as the prophet cut off a piece of wood and threw it into the water. Before their surprised eyes, a miracle! The iron axe floated all the way up to the top of the water!

The student stretched out his arm and picked up the axe. He looked at the prophet in wonder. He had thought he would never see the axe again, and now he was holding it in his hand once more, thanks to another miracle of Elisha.

The students went back to chopping the trees. When the logs were ready, they built a new, large Yeshiva building. Now they had plenty of space to study and pray. They also had a new dining room and rooms to sleep in. How happy everyone was!

✦ 13 ✦
The Frightened Servant

The king of Aram was looking for a way to make trouble for the Jewish people. He came up with an idea. He would capture the king of Israel! He would send men quietly into Israel to set a secret trap for the king to fall into.

With his holy spirit, Elisha knew what the king of Aram was planning. He sent a messenger to Yehoram, warning him, "Beware! The soldiers of Aram have set a trap for you." The messenger told the king exactly where the trap was.

Even though Yehoram had seen Elisha perform miracles, he still did not believe in the power of the prophet. He sent his servants to see if what Elisha said was true. Sure enough, there was a pit, large and deep, covered with branches. If they hadn't listened to Elisha, the king and his men would have fallen into it and been trapped.

The same thing happened over and over again. Each time the soldiers of Aram prepared a new trap, Elisha sent Yehoram a warning to stay away from it.

The king of Aram was fuming. He could not understand why his plan of capturing the king of Israel wasn't working. Maybe there was a spy among his men giving away his secrets. Yes, that must be it!

Calling together his advisors, the king of Aram demanded, "Tell me, which of you is on the side of Israel?"

"My master, the king," one of his advisors answered, "none of us is on the side of Israel. The prophet Elisha knows all your plans, and he warns the king of Israel."

The king was stunned. Far away in Israel, the prophet Elisha knew what he was planning in Aram! Amazing!

"A person like that could really help me," thought the king of Aram. "He could tell me what my enemies are planning. He could help me win wars! I would like him as my chief advisor."

"Go and find out where Elisha is," the king commanded his servants. "I will send for him and take him."

They came back and reported, "Elisha is in the town of Dosan."

Now that the king of Aram knew where the prophet was, he wasted no time in sending his army to capture him.

Quietly, in the dark of the night, soldiers, horses, and chariots surrounded the sleeping town of Dosan. They had come to get Elisha and bring him back with them to Aram.

In middle of the night, Elisha's young servant woke up and went outside. He saw the enemy soldiers surrounding the town. He ran to Elisha, trembling. "Oh, no, my master, what are we going to do?" he asked.

"Don't be afraid," Elisha said. "We have many more on our side than they have on theirs."

But the boy was still afraid.

Elisha felt sorry for him. He prayed, "G-d, open up the boy's eyes so he can see."

G-d opened up the boy's eyes. Around the hills of Dosan he could see fiery angels in the shape of horses and chariots . They were heavenly angels sent to protect Elisha from the enemy. The boy knew they were safe and nothing bad would happen.

G-d had answered Elisha's request and made a miracle just so his young servant should not be scared. Elisha cared about everyone, including a frightened servant boy.

And so another miracle of Elisha had taken place.

Feast in a Time of Famine

The soldiers of Aram surrounding the town of Dosan came closer to where Elisha was. They were going to capture him and bring him to their king!

Elisha did not want to hurt the soldiers of Aram. After all, they were not coming to kill him. But neither did he want to be captured and taken to Aram as the king's chief advisor.

He prayed to G-d, "Please strike these people with confusion."

G-d listened to Elisha's prayer. He made the soldiers confused so they could not understand what was going on.

"This is not the way, and this is not the town you want," the prophet said to the soldiers of Aram. "Follow me, and I will take you to the person you are looking for."

The confused soldiers followed Elisha who led them to the capital city of Shomron. Upon reaching the palace, the holy man prayed, "G-d, open up the eyes of these people so they can see."

G-d opened up their eyes. They were right in front of the palace of the king of Israel.

When Yehoram looked out of the palace window, he couldn't believe what he saw! The enemy soldiers of Aram delivered right into his hands!

"Shall I kill them, my master?" he asked Elisha.

"Is that what you do? Kill captured prisoners?" Elisha asked. "Give them bread and water! Let them eat and drink, and go back to their master in Aram!"

Yehoram ordered a nice meal for them. The soldiers of Aram ate and drank. It was Elisha's way of saying thank you to Aram for wanting him as their advisor.

When they finished eating, Yehoram sent them back to their country.

The king of Aram stopped sending his troops into Israel. For a short while, there was peace.

Whose Fault is this Famine?

Yehoram, king of Israel, had still not done *teshuvah*. He still worshipped idols. He still refused to believe in the prophet though he had seen Elisha perform many miracles.

And so, more trouble came.

After a few months of peace, the king of Aram sent his army to surround the capital city of Shomron. The enemy would not let the Jewish people go in or out of the city. Farmers could not come into the city to sell their crops. There was hardly any food. The people of Shomron were starving.

The little food that was available cost a lot of money. Only the king and the very rich could buy it.

The king took a walk on the wide wall surrounding the city to see how the people were doing.

"Help me, my master, the king!" a woman cried out.

"If G-d is not helping you, how can I?" asked the king bitterly. "From where shall I give you food? From the empty wheat bin or the dry winepress?"

Then Yehoram asked her, "What's the problem?"

The woman told the king how the people were suffering because there was no food. People were dying of hunger.

When Yehoram heard that, he tore his royal clothes. The people saw that underneath he was wearing itchy sackcloth. They realized that although he was not starving, he felt and cared about them.

The king said to himself, "Whose fault is this famine? Elisha's, of course!" If Elisha would ask G-d, G-d would surely end the hunger!

Instead of realizing the famine had come because of his not doing *teshuvah*, Yehoram blamed it on Elisha.

He would punish Elisha! "Elisha's head will not stay on his shoulders for another day!" the king swore.

He sent an officer to carry out his awful threat.

At that moment, Elisha was at his home, speaking to the elders. With his holy spirit he knew what the king had said.

The prophet turned to the elders. "Do you know that that the son of a murderer has sent an officer to cut off my head?" he asked. "When the officer comes, close the door, and push him out with it."

But before they could do anything, Elisha stopped them. "Wait!" he cried out. "I hear the footsteps of his master, the king, coming after him!"

Just then, the officer arrived. Behind him was the king. He was running to catch up to the officer. "Don't kill him!" the king called out. "This famine comes from G-d. If I kill Elisha, it will only make things worse!"

Yehoram realized that the hunger was not Elisha's fault, but his own. He was ready to do *teshuvah*!

The moment Yehoram decided to do *teshuvah*, G-d decreed that the famine would end.

"Listen to the word of G-d!" Elisha cried out to Yehoram.

Everyone grew quiet.

Elisha said to the king, the officer, and all the elders, "This is what G-d said: 'This time tomorrow, one *se'ah* of fine flour will sell for one *shekel*, and two *se'ahs* of barley will sell for half a *shekel* at the gates of Shomron.'"

Food would be cheap! No more hunger! Everyone was so relieved and happy to hear that.

Everyone except the king's officer. "Ha, ha," he mocked. "Is G-d going to make windows in the sky? How can such a thing happen?!"

"You will see it with your own eyes, but you will not get to eat from it," said Elisha angrily.

A Day of Great News

That night Geichazi and his three sons sat outside the gates of Shomron because of their *tzaraat*. They said to each other, "If we stay here, we will die of hunger. On the other hand, if we go into the city, we will also die of hunger, so why don't we go to the enemy camp of Aram? If they give us food, we'll live. If they kill us, well, we'll die here anyway!"

In the middle of the night, they crept to the edge of the enemy's camp. But what a surprise! No one was there! No soldiers, no officers, no generals. The camp was empty!

Where had the army of Aram gone?

A great miracle had just taken place. G-d had made a huge noise that sounded like a vast army was marching towards the camp. The soldiers of Aram were so terrified, they ran away, leaving behind their food, their horses, everything.

G-d had made a miracle so the army of Aram would leave and the famine would be over.

Geichazi and his sons entered the first tent. Nobody was there. But there was food, and plenty of it! They sat down and ate and drank. Then they gathered the gold, silver, and clothing and hid them in a secret hiding place. They went into another tent and did the same there.

But it didn't feel right. The Jews in the city were starving. People could be dying!

"We are not doing the right thing," they said. "It's a day of great news! How can we be quiet and not let everyone know? Besides, if we wait until the morning and don't tell anyone, we'll get into trouble for not telling. So let's tell the king the news right now!"

They went to the keeper of the city gates and said, "We came to the camp of Aram, and there was no one there. The horses and donkeys are all tied up, and the tents are exactly as they were."

The gatekeeper told the news to the palace guards who told it to the king.

The king would not believe it. "The enemy knows we are starving," he said. "Surely they went to hide in the fields, and when we come out, they'll capture us."

One of the servants said, "Why don't you send five men on horses to check it out? It might be dangerous, but we're in danger of starving to death anyway!"

The king agreed, but only to two men. Sure enough, they came back with the news that the army of Aram had fled all the way to the Jordan River, leaving their tents full of food.

The news spread quickly. The hungry people raced out of the city to the empty camp. How much food there was! There was so much that one *se'ah* of fine flour sold for only one *shekel* and two *se'ahs* of barley for only half a *shekel*, exactly as Elisha had said!

The terrible famine was over! Everyone was overjoyed!

The officer who made fun of the prophet was put in charge of the city gates. When the starving people rushed through the gates, he got trampled and died. He was punished because if not for his mocking, Yehoram would have done *teshuvah*.

The officer saw the food, but he never got to eat from it, just as Elisha had said would happen.

Strangers in the House

The siege of Aram was over. The famine had ended. For the last seven years the Shunamis woman had lived in the land of the Plishtim. Her husband had died, and now she came back to the Land of Israel with her son.

When they returned to their home in Shunam, what a surprise they found! Strangers were living in their house!

"This is my house, and this is my field," the woman said to the strangers. "You must leave."

But the strangers would not leave.

The Shunamis woman needed help. She decided to go to the king. Surely, the king could get the strangers out of her house.

When she arrived at the palace, Yehoram was in the middle of asking Geichazi about Elisha. The king had heard that Geichazi had once been a servant of Elisha, and he wanted to ask him about Elisha's other miracles.

But before Geichazi could start speaking, the woman from Shunam and her son entered.

"My master, the king," said Geichazi, "here is the woman, and here is her son whom Elisha brought back to life!"

The woman from Shunam told the king how Elisha had blessed her with a child and how, when the child died, Elisha had brought him back to life.

The king realized she must be a special woman if Elisha had made such miracles for her.

"Why did you come?" he asked her.

"When I returned from the land of Plishtim, I found strangers living in my house," answered the Shunamis woman. "They won't leave. Please can you help me?"

Yehoram turned to his servant. "Get everything back for her," he commanded. "And make sure she is paid for everything that grew in her fields from the time she left the country until now."

The king's servant went with the Shunamis woman and her son to her home. He made the strangers leave the house and pay her for everything that grew in the fields during the last seven years.

The Shunamis woman and her son moved back into their home. Some of the crops she sold, and some she saved. They had plenty of food to eat and money to live on.

14
Elisha Goes to Aram

Elisha had work to do. He had to finish the tasks G-d had given his master Eliyahu. Eliyahu could not do them because he had been taken up to heaven before he could finish them. One of the tasks was to anoint a new king of Aram.

Elisha went to Damesek, the capital city of Aram. But before appointing the new king, there was someone he had to visit: Geichazi. Geichazi had moved to Damesek, far away from the Jewish people.

Elisha felt bad that the man who used to be his servant and student was not living a Jewish life anymore. "Come back and do *teshuvah*," Elisha begged. "Come back to the Jewish people."

"I cannot," said Geichazi. "You taught me that a person who sins and makes others sin cannot do *teshuvah*."

Geichazi had done many bad things after he left Elisha. He had served idols and gotten others to serve them too.

"A Jew can always return to G-d, no matter what," said Elisha.

But Geichazi would not listen.

15
A New King for Aram

The old king of Aram, Ben-Hadad, was very sick. Hearing that the prophet had come to Damesek, he said to his general, "Take a present, and go to the man of G-d. Ask him to tell you what G-d says: Will I get better from this sickness?"

The general took the best things from Damesek to give as a gift to Elisha. Forty camels were needed to carry all the many gifts!

The general, whose name was Chazoel, came before Elisha and said, "Your servant Ben-Hadad, the king of Aram, sent me to ask you: 'Will I live from my sickness?'"

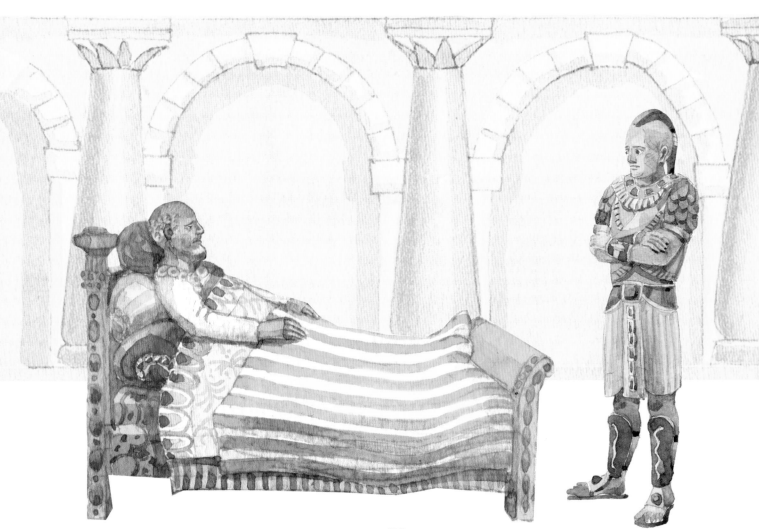

Elisha answered, "Go and say to him, 'You will live.' But G-d has shown me that, in fact, he will die." Elisha wanted the king to think he would live so he should not give up hope.

Suddenly Elisha turned his face away. He tried to hold back his tears, but he could not.

"Why do you cry, my master?" the general asked, surprised.

"I know that as king you will do terrible things to the Jewish people," Elisha said. "You will burn their fortresses and kill their young people cruelly."

"But how can I do those things?" the general asked, surprised. "I'm not a king or anything! I'm just a general!"

"G-d showed me that you are going to be king of Aram," said Elisha.

When the general returned to the palace, Ben-Hadad asked him, "What did Elisha say?"

"He said you will live," Chazoel answered.

Now that Chazoel knew he was supposed to be the next king of Aram, Chazoel did not want to wait. The next day he dipped a thick cloth in cold water and spread it over Ben-Hadad's face. That made the old king even sicker. Soon after that, Ben-Hadad died, and the general was appointed as the new king.

16
Bows and Arrows

Years went by. Yehoram, the king of Israel, had been killed. An arrow of the enemy pierced his heart. This was a punishment for being cruel and threatening to take the children away from Ovadiah's widow.

The name of the new king of Israel was Yoash.

By now Elisha was an old man. But he still prayed for the Jewish people every day and helped them in every way he could.

One day Elisha became sick with his third and last sickness. Yoash, the king, came to see him. When the king realized the prophet would soon pass away, he cried bitterly. "My master, my master, your prayers do more for Israel than chariots and horsemen!" he said, exactly as Elisha had said when Eliyahu went up to heaven.

As Elisha lay dying, he was thinking how he could still help the Jewish people.

He said to the king, "Take a bow and arrows."

Yoash did so.

"Open the window to the east," said Elisha. East was where Aram, the enemy of Israel, was.

The king did so.

"Shoot!" the holy man commanded.

The king shot the arrows out of the window towards Aram.

"The arrows are a sign that G-d will save the Jewish people from the hands of Aram," Elisha said. "You will destroy Aram in the battle of Afek until they are wiped out."

"Take the arrows," Elisha said.

The king did so.

"Hit them on the ground," Elisha commanded.

Yoash hit the arrows on the ground three times and stopped.

"You should have struck the arrows five or six times!" Elisha said, upset. "Then you would have wiped out Aram completely! Now you will only win three times, and you will not wipe out the enemy completely."

Soon after, Elisha passed away. For more than sixty years, he had been the prophet and teacher of the Jewish people. He had helped them in war and in peace through his prayers and his miracles. He took care of everyone from the mighty king to the scared servant boy. He taught thousands of students and worked hard to bring Jews back to G-d.

After Elisha passed away, Israel fought against Aram. Israel won three battles but never won completely, just as Elisha had said.

17
Elisha's Last Miracle

Elisha performed miracles not only when he was alive, but also after he died. Here is how it happened:

There was a man by the name of Shalom, son of Tikvah. Every day he sat at the gates of the city and gave out water to tired and thirsty travelers.

A year after Elisha passed away, Shalom died. From all over Israel, Jews came to the *funeral* of the man who had been so kind.

But just as he was about to be buried, the sound of enemy soldiers was heard. Soldiers from Moav were swooping down on them! There was no time to bury the dead man. The people only had time to open the entrance to the nearest cave and throw Shalom's body inside before they ran away.

Because they were so afraid, the people had not noticed who was buried in that cave. It was none other than the man of G-d, Elisha! Shalom's body rolled over and over. When the body bumped into Elisha, Shalom came back to life!

What a joyful surprise for his wife Chulda and their children when Shalom came home! He lived many more years. He and his wife had another child whom they named Chanamel.

Elisha performed twice as many miracles for the Jewish people as had Eliyahu. Not only that, but Eliyahu had brought one person back to life, while Elisha had brought two, the son of the woman from Shunam and Shalom ben Tikvah.

Eliyahu's promise to Elisha for double his powers had come true.

Glossary

Rosh Chodesh: first day of the new month

Se'ah: a measure

Shekel: a silver coin

Teshuvah: return to G-d

Tzaraat (Metzora): form of impurity, loosely translated as leprosy (leper)

Yeshiva: school for Torah learning

Historical Note

Elisha prophesied during the time of the First Beit Hamikdash beginning in the year 3043 (718 B.C.E.). For six decades he performed wonders for the Jewish people, from the reign of Yehoram, King of Israel, through the next four kings, passing away during the reign of King Yoash.

Other Books by Sterna Citron

For the Family:

**Why the Ba'al Shem Tov Laughed:
52 Stories about our Great Chassidic Rabbis**

Picture Books for Children:

Hirsh's Secret

The Shepherd Boy Who Loved G-d

Shlomo's Little Joke

Zushe's Find

Co-edited with Nechama Dina Smith:

Onions Always Make Me Cry and Other Stories for Teenage Girls

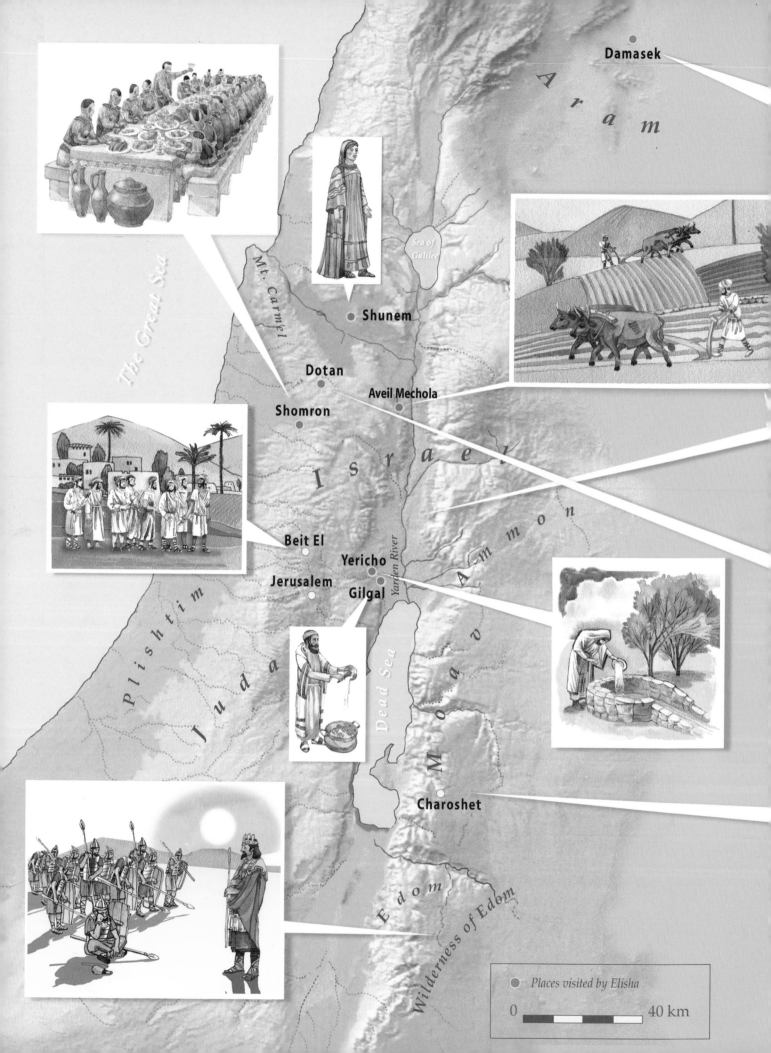

Damasek

A r a m

The Great Sea

Mt. Carmel

Sea of Galilee

Shunem

Dotan

Aveil Mechola

Shomron

I s r a e l

A m m o n

Beit El

Yericho

Yarden River

Jerusalem

Gilgal

Dead Sea

M o a v

Plishtim

Juda

Charoshet

E d o m

Wilderness of Edom

● Places visited by Elisha

0   40 km